Contents

If You Could See Laughter

Hey, it is blue! No, surely red
– the colour of each breath
pumped out by the joy of running,
the jumpstart of a joke.

Tickle-breath is long and spiral.
Pink.
I think.

If you could see laughter
it would look like balloons,
the sort magicians knot in squeaky twists.
Laugh a giraffe.
Guffaw a poodle.

A belly-laugh creates balloons that float.
At the pantomime,
the ceiling of the theatre jostles with colour.
See this baby reaching for the light?
A yellow hiccup of laughter pops out,
floats above us for days.

We could rise off the ground with laughter,
tie strings on it and sail around the world.

Mandy Coe

Words of poetry for:

....

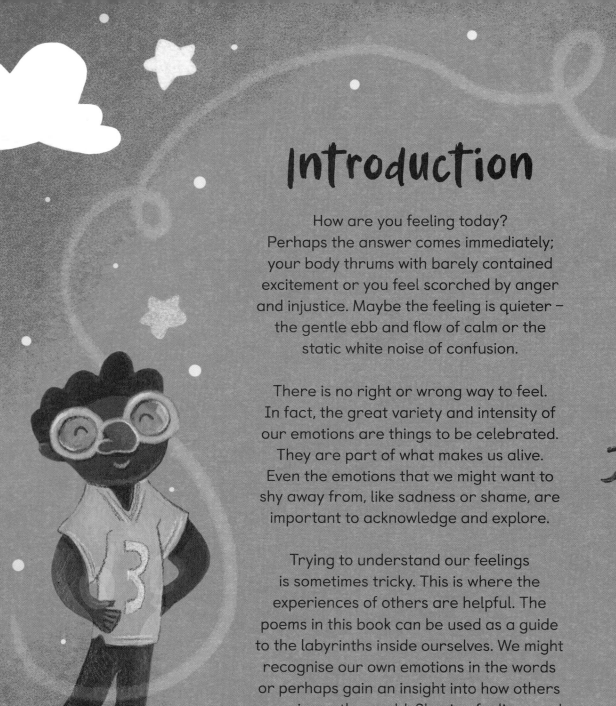

Introduction

How are you feeling today?
Perhaps the answer comes immediately;
your body thrums with barely contained
excitement or you feel scorched by anger
and injustice. Maybe the feeling is quieter –
the gentle ebb and flow of calm or the
static white noise of confusion.

There is no right or wrong way to feel.
In fact, the great variety and intensity of
our emotions are things to be celebrated.
They are part of what makes us alive.
Even the emotions that we might want to
shy away from, like sadness or shame, are
important to acknowledge and explore.

Trying to understand our feelings
is sometimes tricky. This is where the
experiences of others are helpful. The
poems in this book can be used as a guide
to the labyrinths inside ourselves. We might
recognise our own emotions in the words
or perhaps gain an insight into how others
experience the world. Sharing feelings and
reading poetry can bring us together and
create somewhere for hearts and minds to
meet. We hope that this book can be
that place of connection for you.

LiTTLE TiGER

LONDON

The Land of Blue

Across the valley it waits for you,
a place they call The Land of Blue.

It's far and near, it's strange yet known –
and in this land you'll feel alone,
you might feel tears roll down your cheek,
you might feel wobbly, weary, weak.

I know this won't sound fun to you –
it's not – this is The Land of Blue.
It's blue – not gold or tangerine,
it's dark – not light, not bright or clean.

It's blue – and when you leave, you'll see
the crackly branches of the tree,
the golden skies, the purring cat,
the piercing eyes, the feathered hat

and all the other things that come
when you escape from feeling glum.

Across the valley it waits for you,
a place they call The Land of Blue
and going there will help you know
how others feel when they feel low.

Laura Mucha

No More...

I knew the icy grip of fear,
I knew my heart beat like a drum,
I felt a pounding in the ear
And courage crumbling in my tum.

Wolfgang Fang would always scare me.
He used to chase me every day,
Steal my snacks and pocket money.
I'd cry and cry and run away.

I even saw him in nightmares.
But when I learnt my brother too
Was starting school with self-same scares,
We both knew then what we must do...

So we enrolled in martial arts,
Then Wolfgang feared the taste of pain.
Now the bully has fled these parts;
Our school is safe and fun again.

No more the icy grip of fear,
No more heart beating like a drum,
No more a pounding in my ear.
Each kid in school is now our chum.

Debjani Chatterjee

Ache

When teams are picked, for playground games,
I never seem to hear my name.
I stand and watch the choices made
And, one by one, my hopes all fade.
I look around, and force a smile,
Lean on the chain-link fence awhile.
I say, as they all race away,
I didn't really want to play,
But, deep inside the pit of me,
I ache an ache no one can see.

Coral Rumble

Stomp

I come home,
feet about to bleed
from angry stomping.
"Boy!" says Mom.
"Quit making all that racket."
But what does she expect
when, day after day,
haters sling words at me
like jagged stones
designed to split my skin?
I retreat to my room,
collapse on the bed,
count, "One. Two. Three..."
When I get to ten,
I snatch up journal and pen,
flip to a clean page,
and unload my hurt, my rage
'til I can breathe, again.
Letter by letter,
I rediscover
my power to decide
which words matter,
which words don't,
and whose.
Calm, now, I remember:
I get to choose.

Nikki Grimes

12

Touched By Joy

I saw Joy passing in the street,
And everyone she met, she'd greet
With laughter, nods and smiles.
She reached her outstretched hands to me,
Told of the wonders I would see –
Come walk with me awhile.

But Pain was with me, my best friend,
And if our close friendship should end,
I thought I would be lost.
So I let Joy go on her way;
If I should walk with her that day,
I knew Pain would be cross.

Joy came to see me in my school,
In science class, pulled up a stool,
I'm good for you, you know.
You'll be more cheerful, I can tell;
Walk home with me after the bell.
But I just answered, *No!*

For Anger was there by my side,
And I knew he could not abide
Joy's happy voice and face.
So I told Joy she had to leave.
She left and I could not believe
How soon Grief took her place.

I walked home with friends, Doubt and Fear,
To find Joy was already there
With her pals, Love and Dreams.
Come join us, she said, *I insist*,
And I found I could not resist
Their smiles like bright sunbeams.

I hoped my friends would join the fun;
I turned to them, but they had gone
With all the gloom they'd cast.
My heart was light and filled with love
And soaring high, just like a dove,
For I had Joy at last.

Valerie Bloom

15

The Unspeakable Feeling

There are worse things,
of course there are.

Sadness, sickness, shark bites.

But all the same,
I do think there's something
especially appalling
about *embarrassment*.

The hot, rotten throb of it.

The way something
embarrassing
lurks in the brain
like a Jack-in-the-box
that bursts out with a horrible
shriek
all over your thoughts
when you least expect it.

That time I said _____ to _____
and everyone stared.

Or when I fell over the _____
and my _____ came off.

Or when I stood up to do my _____
and I thought it would be
so terrific

but it turned out to be a
terrible, terrible idea
and I wished I could
shrink to the size of a pen lid
and roll under a rug
to be lost for the next
seven-and-a-half years.

That time I _____.
That time I _____.

The thing is,
I suppose
everybody has a moment
when they _____
all over the _____
in front of _____.

And it must haunt them too
like a nasty ghost.

Because it's not just me
walking around with all this
embarrassment, right?

Right?

Somebody?
Anybody?

(Please tell me this isn't going to be
one of those times I _____.)

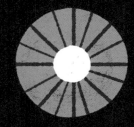

Kate Wakeling

The Hurt Boy and the Birds

The hurt boy talked to the birds
and fed them the crumbs of his heart.

It was not easy to find the words
for secrets he hid under his skin.
The hurt boy spoke of a bully's fist
that made his face a bruised moon –
his spectacles stamped to ruin.

It was not easy to find the words
for things that nightly hissed
as if his pillow was a hideaway for creepy-crawlies –
the note sent to the girl he fancied
held high in mockery.

But the hurt boy talked to the birds
and their feathers gave him welcome –

Their wings taught him new ways to become.

John Agard

19

It's Like This

Like a hot day in February
Like finding a pound coin
in the middle of an empty field
Like bumping into someone legendary
Like discovering an exciting truth
that from you had been concealed

Like walking into your home
to unexpected birthday cheers
Like waking up to your favourite song
tickling your ears

Like being far away from all you know
but walking into someone that's close
Like finding out you're musical
after learning just a few notes

Like waking up from dreaming
and seeing that dream actually happen
Like a gift you never saw coming
and getting what you wanted
and more
after unwrapping

Karl Nova

Lost for Words

Sometimes what people say
isn't what they mean;
when something's really fun
they say that it's a scream.

And when it's raining very hard,
it's *raining cats and dogs,*
but all I see upon the ground
are worms and slugs and frogs.

Apparently they're 'idioms' –
nonsense that makes sense,
not because it's true
but just by general assent.

I tried to make my own up –
said things that were not true,
but I was called a liar
and now I'm feeling *blue*.

That's another one of those,
those things that are not lies –
sayings that mean nothing
and mean everything besides.

I think I'll stick to saying ones
that already exist;
I wouldn't want you all confused,
or *crab, koala, twist*.

Jay Hulme

The Rider

A boy told me
if he roller-skated fast enough
his loneliness couldn't catch up to him,

the best reason I ever heard
for trying to be a champion.

What I wonder tonight
pedaling hard down King William Street
is if it translates to bicycles.

A victory! To leave your loneliness
panting behind you on some street corner
while you float free into a cloud of sudden azaleas,
pink petals that have never felt loneliness,
no matter how slowly they fell.

Naomi Shihab Nye

Talking to Tomorrow

I called out to Tomorrow
To ask about her plan.
She said, "You'll have to wait and see;
Time takes time, you understand?"

So I'm sitting in this secret,
Fizzing with anticipation;
I hope the day is a sentence
With a mark of exclamation!

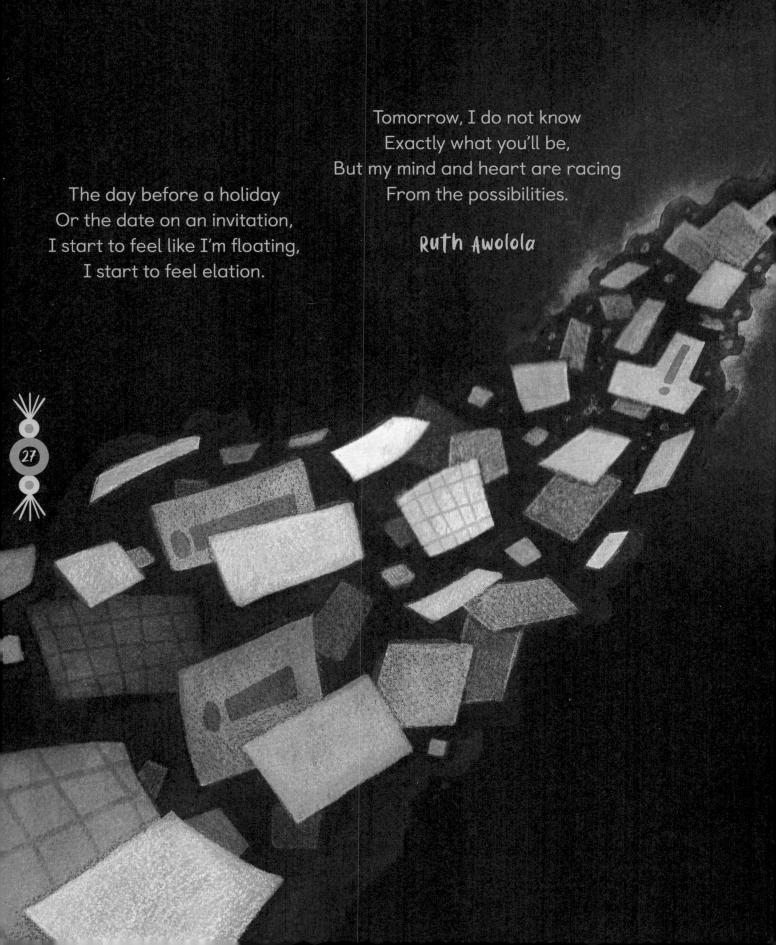

The day before a holiday
Or the date on an invitation,
I start to feel like I'm floating,
I start to feel elation.

Tomorrow, I do not know
Exactly what you'll be,
But my mind and heart are racing
From the possibilities.

Ruth Awolola

27

Losing Face

Finally Mother is proud
Of something
I have done.
"My girl won
The art contest,"
She tells the world,
Smiling so big
And laughing so loud
Her gold tooth
Shows.

I'm the only one who knows
How I drew so well,
Erasing the perfect lines
I traced,
Drawing worse ones
On purpose
In their place.
I feel awful.
I want to tell.

But I don't want to lose
Mother's glowing
Proud face.

Janet Wong

Argument

The monster
With a roar made up of shouts.
Its jaws snap
Like slamming doors.
Its stomach rumbles
Like cars driving away.
Its scales scrape
Like boxes being packed.
Its claws clatter
Like kitchen drawers.

Joseph Coelho

How to Fall Asleep

Hey, Ted, in just a little bit,
we'll need to go to sleep.
So let me show you how.
It's far more fun than counting sheep.

Lie down in bed and close your eyes.
Now take a breath and sigh,
and picture you're an airplane and you're
flying through the sky.

Now fly a little lower through
the clouds and in the breeze,
until you see the water of
the slowly rolling seas.

Then settle on the water where
you've now become a boat,
and feel the ocean rock you
gently, gently as you float.

30

Now turn into a submarine
and sink beneath the waves,
to watch the fish swim in and out
of underwater caves.

You follow them inside,
exploring tunnels as you go.
It's quiet here, and everything
is beautiful and slow.

So you become the water now,
and you become the caves,
and you become the ocean and
the gently rocking waves.

It's peaceful on the ocean bed,
so silent, warm, and deep,
so spread yourself across the world
and drift away to sleep.

Kenn Nesbitt

Homework! Oh, Homework!

Homework! Oh, homework!
I hate you! You stink!
I wish I could wash you
away in the sink,
if only a bomb
would explode you to bits.
Homework! Oh, homework!
You're giving me fits.

32

I'd rather take baths
with a man-eating shark,
or wrestle a lion
alone in the dark,
eat spinach and liver,
pet ten porcupines,
than tackle the homework
my teacher assigns.

Homework! Oh, homework!
You're last on my list,
I simply can't see
why you even exist,
if you just disappeared
it would tickle me pink.
Homework! Oh, homework!
I hate you! You stink!

Jack Prelutsky

Sadness

Sometimes sadness will find you.
It will come to you at dinner or in school,
or after you lose a friend or someone you love.

It will call to you from places
where you don't expect it.

It will make you feel cold
and small and unloved.

When it does,
take its hand.

Tell it that it is okay
to feel small sometimes.

Cry with it and decide together
that it is okay to break sometimes.

Everyone breaks.
Even the ocean.
Even the storm.

When it has told you
everything it needs to,
it will leave.

Remember to gently close
the door after its shadow.

Remember you are still whole,
even after you have broken for a while.

Remember you are still loved,
the same way people still love
the oceans and the storm.

Because no matter how many times
they break, they always
become whole again.

Just like you.

Nikita Gill

35

Blackbird

Let me tell you the secret of flying:
it is to be shameless.

A blackbird on a branch of elder
has no room for shame inside her,
she is so full of song –
and so she rises.

Shame belongs to the worm
squirming in the soil,
scavenged out by beak and scratch
and swallowed whole, digested,
turned to flight.

The blackbird is shameless. She knows shame
settles thick in the bones. She tells you to let go
of all that's heavy:

what you are
what you've done
what's been done to you.

Hop away from it light-footedly
as a thief laughing at the thought of thievery.
Turn a bright black eye skywards
and give yourself to the air.
Leave your shame in the leaf light,
something turquoise and dappled,
something no longer part of you.

The blackbird waits for you in the sky.

See how easy it is to fly?
Easy as weightlessness
or a song in the early morning.

Rachel Plummer

Love You More

Do I love you
to the moon and back?
No I love you
more than that

I love you to the desert sands
the mountains, stars
the planets and

I love you to the deepest sea
and deeper still
through history

38

Before beyond I love you then
I love you now
I'll love you when

The sun's gone out
the moon's gone home
and all the stars are fully grown

When I no longer say these words
I'll give them to the winds, the birds
so that they will still be heard

I
love
you

James Carter

No One Else

Now, someone else can tell you how
To multiply by three
And someone else can tell you how
To spell Schenectady
And someone else can tell you how
To ride a two-wheeled bike
But no one else, no, no one else
Can tell you what to like.

An engineer can tell you how
To run a railroad train
A map can tell you where to find
The capital of Spain
A book can tell you all the names
Of every star above
But no one else, no, no one else
Can tell you who to love.

Your aunt Louise can tell you how
To plant a pumpkin seed
Your cousin Frank can tell you how
To catch a centipede
Your Mom and Dad can tell you how
To brush between each meal
But no one else, no, no one else
Can tell you how to feel.

For how you feel is how you feel
And all the whole world through
No one else, no, no one else
Knows *that* as well as YOU!

Elaine Laron

41

Biographies

Mandy Coe

An award-winning author of eight books, Mandy Coe writes poetry for adults and children. She works in education and on literacy projects through residencies, workshops and readings.

Laura Mucha

Laura Mucha is an ex-lawyer turned award-winning poet and author. Her writing has been featured on TV, radio and public transport, as well as in hospitals, hospices, prisons, books, magazines and newspapers around the world. For more info, visit lauramucha.com

Photo credit: David Yeo

Debjani Chatterjee

Debjani Chatterjee is an Indian-born poet who has written and edited over 70 books, including plays and retellings of traditional tales for children. She is a Fellow of the Royal Society of Literature and Associate Fellow of the Royal Literary Fund. In 2008 she received an MBE.

Coral Rumble

Coral Rumble is a popular, award-winning poet; in 2018 she won The Caterpillar Poetry Prize. She has worked as a poet and performer for many years and now specialises in writing and performing for children.

42

Nikki Grimes

New York Times bestselling author Nikki Grimes is the recipient of the 2020 ALAN Award for outstanding contributions to young adult literature, and the 2017 Children's Literature Legacy Award among other prestigious awards for her distinguished body of children's books.

Valerie Bloom

Winner of the 2022 CLiPPA, Valerie Bloom has written and edited many highly acclaimed children's poetry books; her writing is heavily influenced by her Jamaican background. She has performed widely and appeared on radio and TV. She received an MBE for services to poetry in 2007.

Kate Wakeling

Kate Wakeling grew up in Yorkshire and Birmingham. Her first collection of poems for children, *Moon Juice*, won the 2017 CLiPPA and her second collection, *Cloud Soup*, was a book of the month in the *Guardian* and *The Scotsman*.

Photo credit: Sophie Davidson

John Agard

John Agard was born in Guyana and now lives in the UK. He has published poetry books for adults and children alike and won numerous awards including the BookTrust Lifetime Achievement Award, the CLPE Poetry Award, the Paul Hamlyn Award for Poetry and Queen's Gold Medal for Poetry.

Karl Nova is a hip-hop artist, author and poet. He won the CLiPPA in 2018 for his debut, *Rhythm and Poetry*, and the Ruth Rendell Award 2020 for his influence on literacy in the UK. Karl was born and raised in London and Lagos.

Karl Nova

Palestinian-American poet Naomi Shihab Nye has written books for adults and children, including *Sitti's Secrets* and *Habibi* which both won the Jane Addams Children's Book Award. She was the 2019–2022 Poetry Foundation's Young People's Poet Laureate and received the Ivan Sandrof Lifetime Achievement Award from the National Book Critics Circle in 2020.

Naomi Shihab Nye

Janet Wong is an American poet and children's book author of over 30 titles. She is the co-publisher of Pomelo Books and the winner of the 2021 NCTE Award for Excellence in Poetry for Children, a prestigious lifetime achievement award.

Photo credit: Emily Vardell

Janet Wong

Kenn Nesbitt was born in California and now lives in Washington with his wife and their two cats. He has written over 20 poetry books and was the Poetry Foundation's Children's Poet Laureate 2013–2015.

Kenn Nesbitt

Jay Hulme is an award-winning transgender performance poet, speaker and educator. Jay teaches in schools and consults with groups on the importance of diversity and transgender inclusion in literature and the media.

Jay Hulme

Ruth Awolola is a British-born Nigerian Jamaican poet, workshop facilitator and youth worker. She has been performing poetry since 2015 and was a winner of the national youth slam, SLAMbassadors UK. She has contributed to numerous anthologies including *Rising Stars: New Young Voices in Poetry*.

Ruth Awolola

The 2022–24 Waterstones Children's Laureate, Joseph Coelho is a multi-award-winning children's author and playwright. He writes stage plays, picture books, non-fiction and middle grade. His latest, *The Girl Who Became a Tree,* was shortlisted for the Carnegie Medal.

Photo credit: Hayley Madden/ The Poetry Society

Joseph Coelho

Jack Prelutsky was the USA's first Children's Poet Laureate. He has filled more than fifty books of verse with his inventive wordplay, including the US bestsellers *Scranimals* and *The New Kid on the Block*. He lives in Washington State. You can visit him online at www.jackprelutsky.com.

Photo credit: Skip Kerr

Jack Prelutsky

Nikita Gill is an Irish-Indian poet who has the attention of 600,000 Instagram followers worldwide for her work. She has given a TEDx Talk, spoken at every major literary festival in the UK and been shortlisted for the Goodreads Choice Award in poetry three times. Gill has written seven poetry collections and a novel in verse.

Nikita Gill

Rachel Plummer is a poet based in Edinburgh. They were a Troubadour International Poetry Prize winner in 2014. Their debut children's poetry collection, *Wain*, is based around LGBT retellings of traditional Scottish myths.

Rachel Plummer

James Carter is an award-winning children's poet and an ambassador for the UK's National Poetry Day. He has written many poetry collections, and his verse non-fiction series for Little Tiger Press has been translated into nine languages. www.jamescarterpoet.co.uk

James Carter

Particularly well known for her work on the American children's show *The Electric Company*, Elaine Laron was a songwriter and lyricist. The poem included in this anthology is from the musical children's project *Free to Be... You and Me*.

Elaine Laron

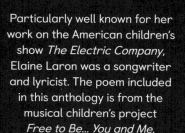

A resident of Columbus, Ohio, Annalise Barber illustrates for children and those who are young at heart. She experiments with sinuous shapes, playful narratives and watercolour media. With a paintbrush in her hand, Annalise illustrates to inspire and empower children.

Annalise Barber

Mariana Roldán is an illustrator based in Mexico. She loves to dance and draw. These activities are how she expresses the feelings that live inside her and how she shares with others the history of the world we live in.

Mariana Roldán

Masha Manapov is an award-winning illustrator, author and image maker. Born in Baku and raised in Tel Aviv, she is currently working from her London-based studio on commissioned projects worldwide.

Masha Manapov

Nabila Adani lives in Jakarta, Indonesia, and enjoys illustrating different world cultures. She briefly worked as a product designer before moving to the United States to study children's book illustration. Now, living back in Jakarta, she enjoys illustrating and telling stories for children worldwide.

Nabila Adani

Copyright and Acknowledgements

CATERPILLAR BOOKS
An imprint of the Little Tiger Group
www.littletiger.co.uk
1 Coda Studios, 189 Munster Road, London SW6 6AW
Imported into the EEA by Penguin Random House Ireland,
Morrison Chambers, 32 Nassau Street, Dublin D02 YH68
First published in Great Britain 2023

This book contains poetry in both British and American English. Though the differences are small, we've chosen to keep all writing in its original dialect. The messages in each poem are for everyone but they are also rooted in the places they were dreamt up and written. We wanted to reflect this.

The Forest Stewardship Council® (FSC®) is an international, non-governmental organisation dedicated to promoting responsible management of the world's forests. FSC operates a system of forest certification and product labelling that allows consumers to identify wood and wood-based products from well-managed forests and other controlled sources.

For more information about the FSC, please visit their website at www.fsc.org